Now, that unholy transmitter's global broadcast has rendered all of mankind docile and helpless against the forces of Apokolips --

-- for embedded in its insidious signal is the ANTI-LIFE EQUATION which obliterates free will and individual identity.

And as the occupying troops of Apokolips fan out over the world, the fate of humanity is now in the hands of a cruel and terrible master.

Above the city, the dark lord of Apokolips surveys his work, and savors the taste of his victory.

WHAT A BEAUTIFUL SIGHT.

FIVE BILLION HUMANS SCATTERED ACROSS SEVEN CONTINENTS, AND EVERY ONE OF THEM MADE SERVILE BY THE POWER OF THE ANTI-LIFE EQUATION.

AND THIS IS ONLY THE BEGINNING, DR. BEDLAM. EARTH IS ONLY THE FIRST WORLD OF THOUSANDS THAT WILL SURRENDER TO ME!

OF THAT I HAVE NO DOUBT, GREAT DARKSEID. HOWEVER, THERE IS STILL THE MATTER OF THE SURVIVING NEW GODS.

THEIR MOTHER BOXES MAKE THEM IMMUNE TO THE SIGNAL.

YOU GOT PROBLEMS WITH THESE MUGS, DARKSEID, LET MY PEOPLE HANDLE IT.

OF COURSE, I'M GONNA NEED SOME MORE OF THESE SPECIAL PLUGS THE DOC PROVIDED TO FILTER OUT THAT CRAZY TRANSMISSION.

RIGHT NOW, ALL MY HEAVY HITTERS ARE OUT OF COMMISSION WITH THE REST OF THE SHEEP.

WHY IS THIS HUMAN *WASTING* MY TIME, BEDLAM?

WAIT A SECOND, PAL, YOU'RE TALKIN' TO *CARLO MANNHEIM*. I RUN INTERGANG, THE NUMBER ONE CRIME SYNDICATE ON THE EAST COAST.

YOU WOULDN'T EVEN BE HERE IF MY ORGANIZATION HADN'T WORKED WITH YOUR BOY BEDLAM TO LAY THE GROUNDWORK FOR THIS *TAKEOVER*.

MISTER MANNHEIM, I SUPPLIED INTERGANG WITH WEAPONS BECAUSE I NEEDED TO GAUGE THE MILITARY AND CIVIL DEFENSE CAPABILITIES OF YOUR WORLD.

NOW THAT I HAVE CONQUERED THIS PLANET, I HAVE NO FURTHER NEED FOR YOU OR INTERGANG. YOU ARE LESS THAN NOTHING TO ME.

LOOK, *BUDDY*, YOU MAY BE THE *BIG CHEESE* ON APOKOLIPS, BUT IN METROPOLIS, *NOBODY* DISRESPECTS CARLO MANNHEIM!

AAGHH!

AS I WAS *SAYING*, BEDLAM, THE UNIVERSE IS *MINE* TO TAKE—NOTHING AND NO ONE CAN STAND IN MY WAY.

AND, GALAXIES AWAY, ON *APOKOLIPS*, THE HARSH AND MERCILESS HOME-WORLD OF EARTH'S NEW MASTER--

YOU SHOULD BE *PROUD*, KAL-EL.

YOU WILL GO TO YOUR GRAVE KNOWING THAT YOU PROVIDED DARKSEID WITH THE MEANS TO CONQUER THE UNIVERSE.

HOW FORTUNATE FOR *APOKOLIPS* THAT THE DEAD SCIENTISTS OF YOUR BIRTH-WORLD ENCODED THE SECRET OF THE *ANTI-LIFE EQUATION* IN YOUR GENETIC CODE.

BLURP
BLURP
BLURP

IS THIS HOW YOU TORTURE *ALL* YOUR VICTIMS, DESAAD... BY *TALKING* THEM TO DEATH?

I DON'T UNDERSTAND *YOU*, KAL-EL. YOU WERE *DARKSEID'S* FAVORED SON, HIS ULTIMATE WARRIOR... HIS *SUPERMAN.*

YET YOU CHOSE TO BETRAY YOUR LORD TO PROTECT A WORLD OF BARELY-EVOLVED *SIMIANS*--

--ALL BECAUSE YOU'VE SUCCUMBED TO THE SIREN VOICE OF THIS ODD-SHAPED MOTHER BOX.

KSPLORS

THE MOTHER BOX ONLY MADE CLEAR WHAT I KNEW IN MY HEART--

--DARKSEID MUST BE STOPPED BEFORE ANOTHER PLANET DIES AT HIS COMMAND.

THEN IT'S A PITY YOU WON'T BE AROUND TO WITNESS WORLD AFTER WORLD CRUSHED BENEATH HIS BOOT HEEL.

OH, DON'T GET ALL WORKED UP. I'M NOT GOING TO KILL YOU YET. FIRST, I'M GOING TO OPEN YOU UP--

BURBLE BU   URBLE BURBLE

Ugh-- NOT CLOSE ENOUGH--

BLAST! I THOUGHT I'D FINALLY FOUND A WAY TO KEEP THE HEAD ALIVE AFTER THE BODY DIED.

NOW, I'D BETTER GET SOME LOWLY TO CLEAN UP THE BLOOD AND GRAY MATTER.

MAYBE. A FRIEND OF MINE GAVE ME SOMETHING CALLED A "MOTHER BOX" WHICH BLOCKS OUT THE SIGNAL.

DAMMIT, THOSE PARADEMONS ARE STILL BEHIND US.

THEN I SAY WE STOP RUNNIN' AND *FIGHT*. I WAS A HEAVYWEIGHT CONTENDER ONCE, Y'KNOW.

I SAW ONE OF THOSE PARADEMONS DISMANTLE A *TANK* WITH ITS BARE HANDS. WE DON'T HAVE A *CHANCE*.

I *DISAGREE*, MADAM.

DARKNESS ALWAYS GIVES WAY TO LIGHT.

YEARGH!

WURGH!

AND THE SOURCE HELPS THOSE WHO HELP THEMSELVES!

HELLO, MISS LANE, AND GREETINGS TO YOU, SIR. I TRUST YOUR RECONNAISSANCE PROVED SUCCESSFUL.

FOR THE LOVE O' MIKE, IT'S AN *ANGEL*. THIS HAS GOTTA BE THE *SCREWIEST* WEEK I EVER HAD!

THIS IS *LIGHTRAY* OF NEW GENESIS, BIBBO. HE'S ONE OF THE FEW GOOD GUYS LEFT. HE'LL LEAD US TO *SAFETY*.

YOU ARE A **BRAVE** WOMAN, LOIS LANE, TO RISK YOUR LIFE BY STANDING WITH US AGAINST DARKSEID.

WE'RE IN THIS TOGETHER. YOU DID WHAT YOU COULD TO TRY TO STOP THE INVASION.

FOR ALL THE GOOD THAT DID US. WHILE WE FOUGHT PARADEMONS AND DOG SOLDIERS, DARKSEID ACTIVATED THE ANTI-LIFE TRANSMITTER.

YEAH, WELL THIS ISN'T GONNA CHEER YOU UP, EITHER. AS BEST AS I COULD DETERMINE, THE ENTIRE PLANET'S IN DARKSEID'S THRALL--

-- EXCEPT FOR THE RARE CASES LIKE **BIBBO** HERE WHO ARE SOMEHOW **IMMUNE** TO THE SIGNAL.

WE CAN'T EXPECT **REINFORCEMENTS.**

WE MUST DESTROY THE ANTI-LIFE TRANSMITTER, BUT EVEN IF WE DO, HOW WILL WE PREVENT DARKSEID FROM RAISING ANOTHER?

IF ONLY HIGHFATHER WERE STILL ALIVE. I FEAR I SHALL LEAD THE NEW GODS TO THEIR **DEATH.**

WE FOLLOW YOU **WILLINGLY,** MY FRIEND, TO WHATEVER END THE SOURCE DECREES.

YOU HAVE YOUR PEOPLE'S **TRUST,** ORION. TRUST **YOUR-** SELF.

AND IF YOU NEED AN EX-PUG FROM SUICIDE SLUM TA KICK SOME **APOCA-** LIPSTICK BUTT, I'M YER **MAN.**

I WISH THIS CRISIS **COULD** BE SOLVED BY **COMBAT** ALONE.

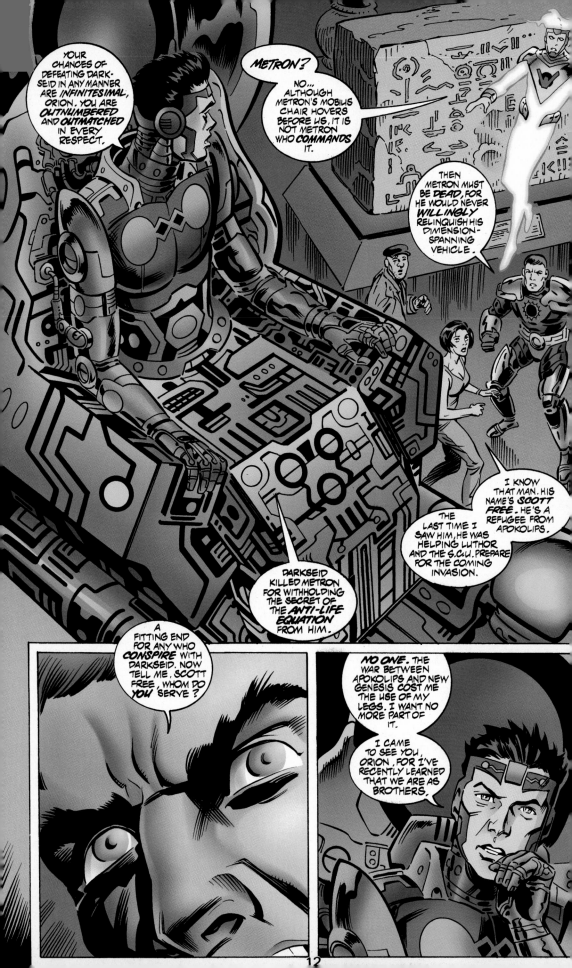

YOUR CHANCES OF DEFEATING DARKSEID IN ANY MANNER ARE *INFINITESIMAL*, ORION. YOU ARE *OUTNUMBERED* AND *OUTMATCHED* IN EVERY RESPECT.

METRON?

NO.... ALTHOUGH METRON'S MOBIUS CHAIR HOVERS BEFORE US, IT IS NOT METRON WHO *COMMANDS* IT.

THEN METRON MUST BE *DEAD*, FOR HE WOULD NEVER *WILLINGLY* RELINQUISH HIS DIMENSION-SPANNING VEHICLE.

I KNOW THAT MAN. HIS NAME'S *SCOTT FREE*. HE'S A REFUGEE FROM APOKOLIPS.

THE LAST TIME I SAW HIM, HE WAS HELPING LUTHOR AND THE S.C.U. PREPARE FOR THE COMING INVASION.

DARKSEID KILLED METRON FOR WITHHOLDING THE SECRET OF THE *ANTI-LIFE EQUATION* FROM HIM.

A FITTING END FOR ANY WHO *CONSPIRE* WITH DARKSEID. NOW TELL ME, SCOTT FREE, WHOM DO *YOU* SERVE?

NO ONE. THE WAR BETWEEN APOKOLIPS AND NEW GENESIS COST ME THE USE OF MY LEGS. I WANT NO MORE PART OF IT.

I CAME TO SEE YOU, ORION, FOR I'VE RECENTLY LEARNED THAT WE ARE AS BROTHERS.

12

BROTHER? I HAVE NO BROTHER.

I SPEAK *METAPHORICALLY.* WE WERE BOTH *PAWNS* IN OUR FATHERS' GAME OF WAR.

DO YOU KNOW THE DARK SECRET OF THE *PACT* THAT CREATED THE SHORT-LIVED *TRUCE* BETWEEN NEW GENESIS AND APOKOLIPS?

NO, OF COURSE YOU DON'T. YOU WERE KEPT AS MUCH IN THE DARK AS I WAS.

"TO SEAL THE PACT BETWEEN THE TWO WARRING WORLDS, DARKSEID AND HIGHFATHER AGREED TO EXCHANGE THEIR FIRST-BORN CHILDREN.

"HIGHFATHER ALLOWED HIS INFANT SON TO BE RAISED ON APOKOLIPS WHERE THE BOY SUFFERED EVERY ABUSE IMAGINABLE.

"AT THE SAME TIME, DARKSEID'S SON WAS RAISED BY HIGHFATHER WITH THE LOVE GIVEN EVERY NEW GENESIS CHILD.

"NEITHER CHILD WAS TOLD THE TRUE IDENTITY OF HIS FATHER, BUT AS I AM THE CHILD OF HIGHFATHER, *YOU* ARE THE *SON* OF *DARKSEID.*"

LIAR!

I DIDN'T INTEND TO ANGER YOU. I ONLY WISHED TO ENLIGHTEN YOU TO THE TRUTH THAT WAS DENIED US FOR TOO LONG.

SKRASH

NO, THIS IS SOME CRUEL *DECEPTION*. DARKSEID *CANNOT* BE MY FATHER.

BELIEVE WHAT YOU WILL. THIS CONFLICT IS NO LONGER MY CONCERN. I HAVE THE UNIVERSE TO EXPLORE.

FAREWELL. WE SHALL NOT MEET AGAIN.

ORION IS DARKSEID'S SON?

BY THE SOURCE...

IF YOU HAVE SOMETHING TO SAY, SAY IT TO MY *FACE!*

CALM DOWN, MY FRIEND. THOUGH THIS REVELATION IS *SURPRISING*, IT DOESN'T *DIMINISH* OUR FAITH IN YOU.

I'VE ALWAYS KNOWN THE FIRES OF APOKOLIPS BURN IN MY VEINS, BUT I THOUGHT I COULD CONTROL THAT PART OF ME--

--BUT NOW IT'S CLEAR MY EFFORTS HAVE BEEN IN VAIN.

NOBILITY IS DEFINED BY *DEEDS*, NOT BLOODLINE.

NO! IF I AM TRULY DARKSEID'S SPAWN, THEN I AM *CURSED*. I WILL ONLY LEAD THE PEOPLE OF NEW GENESIS TO *RUIN!*

ORION!

HALL OF ANTIQ

LET HIM GO, LIGHTRAY. HE HAS TO COME TO TERMS WITH THIS ON HIS *OWN*.

AND IF HE DOESN'T, THEN WE HAVE EVEN LESS THAN A SNOWBALL'S CHANCE IN HELL AGAINST DARKSEID.

FROM APOKOLIPS, THERE IS ONLY ONE WAY TO CROSS THE INORDINATE DISTANCE TO EARTH, AND THAT IS VIA THE EXTRA-DIMENSIONAL PORTALS CALLED *BOOM TUBES*.

DAMN. THIS BLASTED MACHINE REFUSES TO RECOGNIZE MY COMMANDS.

YOU SHOULD KNOW BETTER, CHILD. NO ONE LEAVES APOKOLIPS WITHOUT *MY* PERMISSION.

IF ONLY YOU'D BEEN SENT TO MY ORPHANAGE AS A CHILD, YOU'D KNOW BETTER THAN TO *TALK BACK* TO YOUR GRANNY.

IF THERE'S ONE THING THAT GRANNY WILL NOT *TOLERATE*, IT'S INSOLENCE.

ISN'T THAT *RIGHT*, LEX?

MMRRRFFF!

YOU DON'T WANT TO *INTERFERE* WITH ME, OLD WOMAN.

TAKE HIM, MY LITTLE *DARLINGS*. SHOW HIM THE COST OF SUCH WILLFUL *DISOBEDIENCE*.

KRAK

BARDA! I'M GLAD TO SEE THAT YOU SURVIVED THE AMBUSH OVER METROPOLIS HARBOR.

OF COURSE I **SURVIVED.** I'M A HARD WOMAN TO **KILL.** AND THEY WERE ONLY HUMAN SOLDIERS AFTER ALL.

DO YOU INTEND TO STOP ME FROM RETURNING TO EARTH?

NO. AFTER THE INVASION, DARKSEID ORDERED ALL THE FURIES BACK TO APOKOLIPS TO MAINTAIN ORDER IN HIS ABSENCE--

--BUT ONCE HE BUILDS AN ANTI-LIFE TRANSMITTER HERE, HE'LL HAVE NO MORE USE FOR HIS WARRIOR ELITE. WE ARE OBSOLETE.

HIS DESIRE FOR ABSOLUTE CONTROL MEANS THAT THERE IS NO PLACE SAFE FROM HIM.

ENOUGH OF DARKSEID. WHAT DO **YOU** DESIRE, KAL-EL?

TO PUT AN END TO DARKSEID'S USE OF THE ANTI-LIFE EQUATION.

THAT'S WHY I NEED THE CONTROL CODES FOR THE BOOM TUBE GENERATOR.

FORGET ABOUT **EARTH.** IT BELONGS TO DARKSEID NOW. WHY NOT GO AWAY WITH ME INSTEAD?

YOU AND I ARE WARRIORS BORN. LET US FIND SOME DISTANT WORLD TO CONQUER IN GLORIOUS **BATTLE.**

EVEN THE MOST DISTANT WORLD WILL ONE DAY FALL UNDER DARKSEID'S SHADOW.

IF I DON'T STOP DARKSEID ON EARTH, THERE WILL BE NO MORE GLORIOUS BATTLES FOR EITHER OF US.

GIVE ME THE **CODE,** BARDA.

17

THANK YOU.

YOU KNOW THAT IF YOU CONFRONT DARKSEID DIRECTLY YOU WILL *DIE*. EVEN UNDER A *YELLOW* SUN, YOU ARE NOT THAT STRONG.

BOOM!

I HAVE COME TO BELIEVE THAT *LIFE* AND *FREEDOM* ARE WORTH THAT RISK.

YOU'RE A *STRANGE* AND *STUBBORN* MAN, KAL-EL. SINCE THERE'S NO POINT IN TRYING TO *SWAY* YOU FROM THIS *SUICIDAL* COURSE--

--PERHAPS I CAN GIVE YOU *ONE GOOD* REASON TO *SURVIVE.*

GOOD LUCK, KAL-EL.

AT THE END OF TIME AND SPACE LIES THE **PROMETHEAN WALL**, THE BOUNDARY BETWEEN THE PHYSICAL UNIVERSE AND THE UNKNOWN COSMIC FORCES THAT BIRTHED THAT UNIVERSE.

IS IT CURIOSITY THAT HAS BROUGHT SCOTT FREE HERE-- OR SOME **GREATER DESIGN**?

IN MY SHORT TRAVELS, I HAVE ALREADY WITNESSED THE BIRTH OF WORLDS AND THE DEATH OF STARS, BUT NOTHING COMPARES TO THIS.

BEFORE ME ARE THE **PROMETHEAN GIANTS**--GODS OF A THOUSAND MYRIAD WORLDS.

EACH DEITY ONCE SOUGHT TO BREACH THE WALL AND ENTER THE VERY HEART OF THE **SOURCE**-- --AND EACH PAID A HEAVY PRICE FOR THEIR HUBRIS, FOR THEY MUST NOW SPEND ETERNITY AS PART OF THE WALL.

HERE IS THE WARRIOR GOD **WOTAN**, WHO RULED THE PANTHEON OF THE FIRST WORLD, AND WHO SACRIFICED AN EYE FOR **OMNISCIENCE**.

DID YOU PROPHESY THIS MOMENT, OLD ONE?

DID YOU FORESEE THAT THROUGH YOU, THE MASTER OF THE MOBIUS CHAIR WOULD ONE DAY ACCESS THE GREAT MYSTERY YOU GUARD?

SOON, THE ANSWERS TO THE UNIVERSE WILL BE MINE...

GREAT INFINITY! I HAD NO IDEA IT WOULD BE LIKE THIS...

19

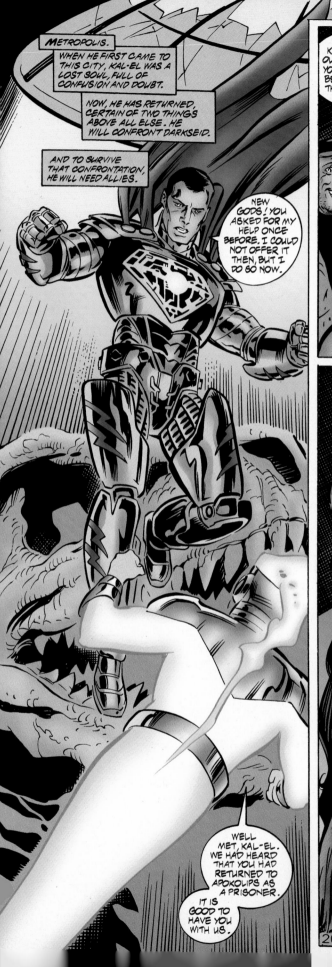

METROPOLIS.
WHEN HE FIRST CAME TO THIS CITY, KAL-EL WAS A LOST SOUL, FULL OF CONFUSION AND DOUBT.

NOW, HE HAS RETURNED, CERTAIN OF TWO THINGS ABOVE ALL ELSE. HE WILL CONFRONT DARKSEID.

AND TO SURVIVE THAT CONFRONTATION, HE WILL NEED ALLIES.

NEW GODS! YOU ASKED FOR MY HELP ONCE BEFORE. I COULD NOT OFFER IT THEN, BUT I DO SO NOW.

WELL MET, KAL-EL. WE HAD HEARD THAT YOU HAD RETURNED TO APOKOLIPS AS A PRISONER.

IT IS GOOD TO HAVE YOU WITH US.

GLAD KAL'S ON OUR SIDE. YOU WOULDN'T BELIEVE WHAT THAT GUY CAN DO.

YOU'VE CHANGED, KAL. IT'S NOT JUST THE ARMOR. IT'S SOMETHING IN YOUR EYES. A SENSE OF DETERMINATION.

MAYBE WE DO HAVE A CHANCE AGAINST DARKSEID AFTER ALL.

HE DESTROYED NEW GENESIS. HE BRINGS NOTHING BUT DEATH.

MOONRIDER'S RIGHT. WHAT'S THE POINT IN FIGHTING ANY LONGER?

HAS THE SOURCE FORSAKEN US?

YOUR CHANGE OF HEART COMES TOO LATE TO DO US ANY *GOOD*, SUPERMAN.

LOOK AROUND. HALF OUR NUMBER ARE DEAD. ORION HAS ABANDONED US. DARKSEID HAS *WON*.

I KNOW I CAN NEVER ATONE FOR THE DESTRUCTION OF YOUR PLANET, BUT I'LL DO WHATEVER IT TAKES TO STOP DARKSEID HERE AND NOW.

I THINK WE SHOULD WRITE THIS PLANET OFF AS LOST, AND START LOOKIN' FOR REINFORCEMENTS SOMEWHERE ELSE.

YOU WANT TO THROW IN THE TOWEL, SERIFAN, GO AHEAD. NOT ME. THIS IS MY HOME.

I'D RATHER GO DOWN FIGHTING THAN GIVE UP! AFTER ALL, NOBODY LIVES FOREVER!

HIGHFATHER KNEW THAT OUR BEST HOPE OF STOPPING DARKSEID WAS HERE ON EARTH. WE MUST ACT NOW.

YOU GOT A PLAN, BIG MAN?

YES, BUT TO SUCCEED, I WILL NEED ALL OF YOU.

FIFTH AVENUE.

WHAT NEED HAS DARKSEID FOR SOLDIERS OR ASSASSINS NOW THAT HE HAS THE MEANS TO ENSLAVE A WORLD IN THE SPACE OF MINUTES?

WHAT OPPOSITION IS LEFT FOR US TO QUELL?

UND DIE NEU GOTTS?*

*AND THE NEW GODS?

ONCE WE ROUND UP THE LAST OF THE NEW GENESIS REFUGEES WE'LL HAVE NOTHING LEFT TO--

--STEPPENWOLF'S GHOST!

VAS IS DAS?

THE SKY!

HOW CAN YOU ENJOY THIS, VUNDABAR? IF YOU WEREN'T SO BUSY POSTURING AND PREENING LIKE SOME PRUSSIAN POPPINJAY--

--YOU'D UNDERSTAND THAT THE ANTI-LIFE TRANSMITTER SIGNALS THE END FOR YOU AND ME.

NEIN. NEIN.

IT IS UNFORTUNATE NEITHER OF YOU POSSESS THE SENSORY INPUT DEVICES OF MY MECHANICAL BODIES--

--OTHERWISE YOU WOULD BE AWARE THAT YOU ARE VICTIMS OF A POWERFUL ILLUSION DESIGNED TO CONCEAL AN ATTACK.

AT LAST, A BATTLE WORTHY OF MY TALENT...

23

KCHOOM

<ATTACK!>

YOU RELY TOO MUCH ON *TOYS*, VUNDABAR.

TOYS CAN BE *BROKEN*.

BA-KRASH

DIE, NEW GODS! DIE!

FORWARD, MY BROTHERS AND SISTERS! THOUGH ALL OF APOKOLIPS MAY STAND IN OUR WAY, WE MUST REACH THE ANTI-LIFE TRANSMITTER!

BUT, LIGHTRAY, THE PARADEMONS AND AEROTROOPERS *OUTNUMBER* US BY *TENFOLD!*

THEN FIGHT *TEN* TIMES AS HARD, ESAK. IF WE FAIL TODAY, WE CONDEMN A *THOUSAND* WORLDS TO DARKSEID'S CRUELTY.

24

HMMM.

DO NOT UNDERESTIMATE THE LORD OF APOKOLIPS, KAL-EL. THOUGH HE ALLOWS ARMIES TO FIGHT FOR HIM, HE IS A FORMIDABLE WARRIOR.

SO AM I.

HEAR ME, DARKSEID! I AM COMING FOR YOU!

BRAVO, KAL-EL. I DID NOT EXPECT TO SEE YOU AGAIN.

IT WILL TAKE MORE THAN THAT SADIST DESAAD TO STOP ME.

YES, I TAUGHT YOU WELL, BUT NOT WELL ENOUGH, IT SEEMS, OR YOU WOULD NEVER HAVE RETURNED TO FIGHT A BATTLE YOU CANNOT WIN.

LOOK BELOW YOU. YOUR NEW ALLIES HAVE NO HOPE OF DEFEATING MY TROOPS.

ONE BY ONE, THEY WILL DIE, UNTIL FINALLY THE CHILDREN OF NEW GENESIS WILL BE AS DEAD AS THE PLANET ON WHICH THEY WERE BORN.

VUNDABAR CAN KEEP HIS MONSTROUS TANKS AND CANNONS. THERE IS NO ART TO *BLUDGEON-ING* AN OPPONENT FROM A DISTANCE.

I PREFER THE INTIMACY OF A FINELY-HONED BLADE. DON'T YOU?

HURGHH!

THE ATROCITIES YOU'VE COMMITTED IN DARKSEID'S NAME END HERE, DOCTOR BEDLAM.

LIGHTRAY, UNLIKE YOU, I'M NOT LIMITED TO JUST ONE BODY. I HAVE *THOUSANDS*--

AS YOU SEE, THE NEW *GODS* HAVEN'T A PRAYER AGAINST ME.

STILL, IN VICTORY, I AM INCLINED TO BE *GENEROUS*. LEAVE NOW, FLY AS FAST AND FAR AS YOU CAN, AND YOU MAY *LIVE*.

NEVER!

I'LL DO WHATEVER IT TAKES TO STOP YOU FROM TURNING THE ANTI-LIFE EQUATION ON ANOTHER WORLD.

AND I'LL BEGIN BY ELIMINATING THE TRANS-MITTER.

AND I THOUGHT *KALIBAK* WAS MY IDIOT CHILD. NOW YOU'VE FORCED ME TO ELIMINATE *YOU*.

--AND I MOVE BETWEEN MY MECHANICAL HOSTS WITH THE SPEED OF THOUGHT.

NO!

URGHH!

K-CHOOM

<DIE, BIG BEAR!>

THE NEW GODS ARE BEING PICKED OFF LIKE FLIES! IT WAS INSANE TO ATTACK DARKSEID'S FORCES DIRECTLY!

SHOULDN'T HAVE GOTTEN MY HOPES UP WHEN KAL-EL RETURNED!

BUH-ROOM

YEARGH!

YOUR OMEGA BEAMS DID NOT KILL ME...

...IT SEEMS THAT IT IS MORE THAN THIS ARMOR THAT GIVES ME STRENGTH.

YOUR KRYPTONIAN PHYSIOLOGY MAY MAKE YOU STRONGER UNDER THIS PLANET'S SUN--

--BUT I PROMISE YOU, IT DOES NOT MAKE YOU INVINCIBLE.

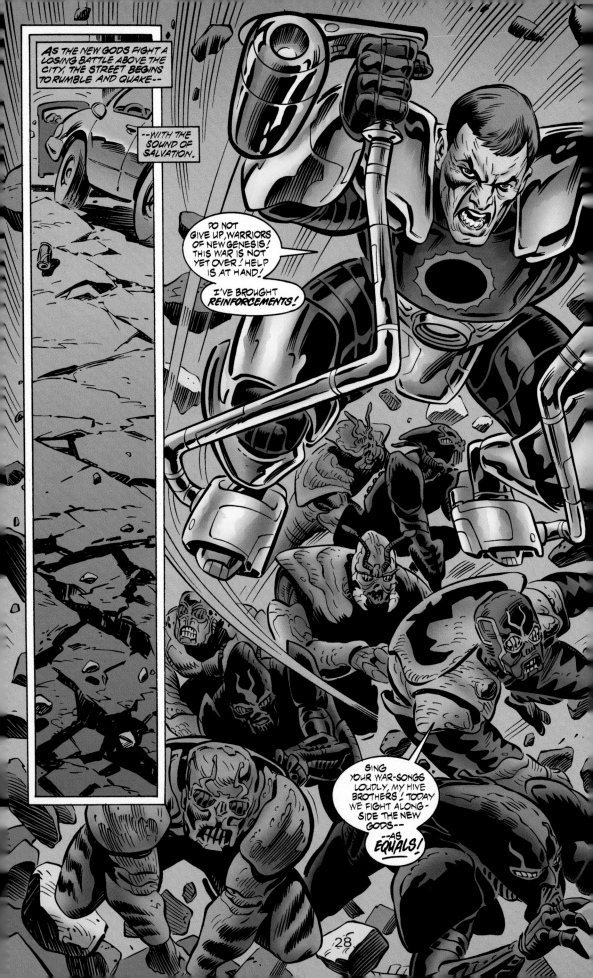

29

AMAZING!

I WOULDN'T HAVE BELIEVED IT POSSIBLE, BUT THOSE BUGS ACTUALLY DID WHAT WE COULD NOT AND *SHUT DOWN* THE TRANSMITTER!

DARKSEID'S UNHOLY ANTI-LIFE BROADCAST HAS ENDED!

NOW, ALL THAT *REMAINS* IS FOR ME TO PUT AN *END* TO THIS ABOMINATION *ONCE* AND FOR *ALL!*

KRAKAKROOOOM!!

IT'S *OVER*, DARKSEID.

SOON HUMANITY WILL AWAKEN FROM ITS DRUGGED STATE, AND THEN TAKE *ARMS* AGAINST YOUR FORCES.

DO YOU TRULY THINK I CANNOT BUILD ANOTHER ANTI-LIFE TRANSMITTER-- OR A THOUSAND FOR THAT MATTER?

THIS SMALL VICTORY IS A MOMENTARY *INCONVENIENCE*, NOTHING MORE.

YOU'RE *WRONG!* IT IS THE BEGINNING OF THE END FOR YOU, MY *FATHER!*

I KILLED MY OWN FATHER. I'VE NO INTENTION OF SUFFERING THE SAME FATE!

BEHOLD THE ANTI-MOTHER BOX. NO MOTHER BOX CAN WITHSTAND THE DESTRUCTIVE ENERGIES IT EMITS.

AHH...

HUGHH!

SKRZZAK

SKRZAK

ORION!

ORION, CAN YOU HEAR ME? *TALK* TO ME!

MOTHER BOX... CONNECTED TO... MY... SOUL...

...WHEN SHE DIED...PART... OF ME...DID... TOO...

31

ORION DEPENDED ON HIS MOTHER BOX MORE THAN I DID, DARKSEID. I CAN DEFEAT YOU WITHOUT MINE.

UHF

KAROOM

YOU'VE EXHAUSTED MY GOODWILL, KAL-EL.

NOW, YOU'VE FORCED MY HAND!

THWEK

UGHH!

NEVER HAVE I FELT SUCH A BLOW!

PAIN MAKES IT HARD TO CONCENTRATE AND STAY AIRBORNE...

KRONCH

32

LOIS LANE, YOU'RE RISKING YOUR LIFE OUT IN THE OPEN LIKE THIS. TAKE COVER.

WHAT'S THE *USE?* I MEAN, I'VE TRIED TO BE A GOOD SOLDIER THROUGH ALL OF THIS INSANITY-- BUT WHO AM I KIDDING?

EVEN WITH THE TRANSMITTER DOWN, WE'D NEED A MIRACLE TO OVERCOME DARKSEID'S FORCES.

I CANNOT DENY OUR PRESENT SITUATION IS DIRE, BUT I REFUSE TO ACCEPT DEFEAT.

WHILE THERE IS LIFE, THERE IS HOPE.

EVER THE OPTIMIST, LIGHTRAY. EVEN IN THE FACE OF IMMINENT ANNIHILATION...

SCOTT FREE? WHY HAVE YOU RETURNED? DO YOU FIND PLEASURE IN THIS CARNAGE?

NO. SINCE I LEFT THIS PLANET, I HAVE TRAVELED TO THE ENDS OF THE COSMOS AND LEARNED WHAT LIES BEYOND THE *PROMETHEAN WALL.*

I HAVE WITNESSED THE TRUE NATURE OF THE UNIVERSE, AND BEEN BLINDED BY ITS MAGNIFICENCE.

YEAH, WELL, WHEN YOU GET YOUR TRAVEL PHOTOS DEVELOPED, BRING THEM BY--

--BUT RIGHT NOW, UNLESS YOU'RE WILLING TO HELP US, YOU'RE WASTING OUR TIME.

YES, YOU ARE RIGHT. THERE IS LITTLE TIME LEFT TO TURN THIS BATTLE.

LIGHTRAY, LISTEN TO ME. THE KRYPTONIAN IS, LIKE YOU, A CHILD OF THE LIGHT.

YOUR **TOUCHING** CHANGE OF HEART WILL NOT **SAVE** THE NEW GODS FROM **OBLIVION**, SCOTT FREE.

YOU'VE MERELY INSURED YOUR OWN DEATH BY RETURNING.

SO **BE** IT. MY SPIRIT WAS ONCE SHACKLED WITH ANGER AND RESENTMENT, BUT NO MORE.

I HAVE SEEN THE SOUL OF THE UNIVERSE, AND THAT VISION HAS **LIBERATED** MY HEART.

SPARE ME YOUR **NOXIOUS PLATITUDES.** YOU SOUND FAR TOO MUCH LIKE YOUR BIRTH FATHER.

IF SCOTT FREE IS **CORRECT**, AND KAL-EL, TOO, DRAWS **SUSTENANCE** AND **STRENGTH** FROM STARLIGHT--

--THERE IS A CHANCE I CAN **RESUSCITATE** HIM WITH THE **PHOTO-VOLTAIC** ENERGY MY BODY **GENERATES.**

FOR THE SAKE OF THE UNIVERSE, KAL-EL, **LIVE.**

HRRNNHMM... TURN AND **FACE** ME, DARKSEID... WE'RE NOT **FINISHED**...

35

YOU'RE WRONG.

THE ENERGY I PROVIDED KAL-EL WAS *INSUFFICIENT.* HE'LL NEVER SURVIVE AGAINST DARKSEID UNLESS I GIVE HIM MORE--

KRAK

YOU WILL DO NOTHING BUT DIE, NEW GOD!

AARGH!

DARKSEID IS VICTOR--

ENOUGH, DOCTOR BEDLAM.

WHAT'S... HAPPENING... TO... ME?

I HAVE IMPRISONED YOUR *BODY-HOPPING* CONSCIOUSNESS IN THIS PSIONIC CONTAINMENT UNIT, DOCTOR.

UNFORTUNATELY THE MOBIUS CHAIR'S SENSORS DID NOT REGISTER YOUR PRESENCE UNTIL IT WAS *TOO LATE* FOR LIGHTRAY.

ORION... MY OLD FRIEND,... IT APPEARS THAT WE ARE NOT *INVINCIBLE* AS WE THOUGHT.

LIGHTRAY?

36

HEART OF THE CITY

BY LOIS LANE
DAILY PLANET
STAFF WRITER

It's been a year since the occupation, and Metropolis is still cleaning up the damage done during that nightmarish time...

...NOW TED GRANT... THERE WAS A BOXER--ME AND HIM WENT ELEVEN ROUNDS ONCE BACK IN THE DAY...

...OO WEE... HE SURE CLEANED MY CLOCK IN THE END...

UH, UH, MISTAH BIBBO... MISTAH BIBBO...

SPIT IT OUT, SCRAPPER!

LOOK OUT!

WHAT THE--?!

HOLD ON, JIMMY...

GEEZ, LOUISE!

I SWEAR, SERENA, I'M NEVER GONNA GET THE HANG OF THESE CRAZY DISCS--

ONCE YOU GET YOUR BALANCE, YOU'LL BE FINE. PROMISE.

AW, WHAT'S THE USE OF GIVING 'EM GRIEF? KIDS'LL BE KIDS.

HEY, YOU CRAZY KIDS-- WHY DON'T YOU WATCH--

...but we Metropolitans are a resilient crowd, and we've managed to adjust to the changes in our fair city.

Not the least of which is the presence of the city's newest borough...

...The airborne city launched into geosynchronous orbit above the harbor by the New Gods.

While there won't be rail service to the airborne city, my sources tell me that shuttle service will soon be available.

It appears that Metropolis is no longer just an international city. It's an intergalactic one.

IT'S ASTOUNDING! HOW DID YOU BUILD IT SO QUICKLY?

THE BUGS ARE REMARKABLY INDUSTRIOUS WORKERS. THEY'VE HELPED IMMEASURABLY BOTH WITH CONSTRUCTION AND DESIGN. I AM EMBARRASSED TO SAY I USED TO THINK OF THEM AS ANIMALS.

YOU'VE CHANGED. WE ALL HAVE.

EVERY DAY. HE WAS THE *TRUEST* OF FRIENDS. HE SAW IN ME THE THINGS I COULD NOT SEE MYSELF.

IF ONLY LIGHTRAY WERE HERE TO SEE THE BEGINNING OF THIS NEW AGE.

YOU *MISS* HIM, DON'T YOU?

LIGHTRAY

I THINK HE'D BE *PROUD* OF WHAT YOU'VE ACCOMPLISHED HERE, ORION.

IT'S NOTHING COMPARED TO WHAT KAL-EL IS DOING ON APOKOLIPS.

THEN THE RUMORS I'VE HEARD ARE TRUE!

YES. HE'S DONE WHAT SOME WOULD CALL IMPOSSIBLE.

I NEVER WOULD HAVE IMAGINED HE WOULD BECOME SUCH A... SUPERMAN.

WHEN I FIRST MET HIM, HE WAS SO UNDENIABLY POWERFUL, AND AT THE SAME TIME, SEEMED SO VERY LOST.

THE SAME COULD BE SAID OF ME.

WE WERE BOTH RAISED IN *DARKNESS*, AND HAVE SPENT OUR LIVES *FUMBLING* TOWARDS THE *LIGHT*.